The Red Ear Blows Its Nose

The Red Ear
Blows Its Nose

Poems for Children and Others

BY
Robert Schechter

ILLUSTRATED BY
S. Federico

WORD GALAXY PRESS
An imprint of Able Muse Press

Word Galaxy Press

www.wordgalaxy.com

Library of Congress Cataloging-in-Publication Data

Names: Schechter, Robert, 1955- author. | Federico, S., 2001- illustrator.
Title: The red ear blows its nose : poems for children and others / by Robert Schechter ; illustrated by S. Federico.
Description: San Jose, CA : World Galaxy Press, an imprint of Able Muse Press, 2023. | Audience: Ages 7-12. | Audience: Grades 2-7.
Identifiers: LCCN 2022035887 (print) | LCCN 2022035888 (ebook) | ISBN 9781773491301 (paperback) | ISBN 9781773491349 (hardcover) | ISBN 9781773491318 (ebook)
Subjects: LCSH: Children's poetry, American. | CYAC: American poetry. | LCGFT: Poetry.
Classification: LCC PS3619.C3384 R43 2023 (print) | LCC PS3619.C3384 (ebook) | DDC 811/.6--dc23/eng/20220805
LC record available at https://lccn.loc.gov/2022035887
LC ebook record available at https://lccn.loc.gov/2022035888

Printed in the United States of America

Cover image: *The Red Ear and Friends* by S. Federico

Cover & book design by S. Federico and Alexander Pepple

Word Galaxy Press is an imprint of Able Muse Press—at
www.ablemusepress.com

Word Galaxy Press
467 Saratoga Avenue #602
San Jose, CA 95129

for

Susannah and Lincoln

(obviously)

Acknowledgments

My grateful acknowledgments go to the editors of the following publications where these poems, some in earlier versions, first appeared:

Alabama Literary Review: "Lights Out," "My First Snow," and "Reaching Six"

Anon Two: "My Champion Bee," "Obviously," "Solar Lunacy," and "The Thing about Chickens"

Asses of Parnassus: "Question"

The Best Ever Book of Funny Poems: "What's Mine"

Bumbershoot: "I'm Igserious," "The Chorus of Doris," "The Horse Who Said *Moo*," and "Unlucky"

The Caterpillar: "Bird Talk," "It's All Me," "Just Wondering," "My Brain," "They Say," and "We Come in Peace"

Cricket: "The Breeze" and "Instrumental"

Dirigible Balloon: "Summer Sorcerer"

Highlights: "Colors," "How High Is the Sky," "Popcorn Dream," "Sky," and "Under the Rainbow"

Ladybug: "Reading between the Letters" and "To and Fro"

Light Quarterly: "Jokes Talk Back"

One Minute till Bedtime: 60-Second Poems to Send You Off to Sleep: "The Just-Because Hug"

The School Magazine: "Brain Break," "Dancing," "Fabulous Five," "My Nose," "Talking to the Wall," "Breezy Does It," and "Winning"

Spaced Out: Space Poems Chosen by Brian Moses and James Carter: "Bang!"

The Spectator: "Winter's Tale"

Spider: "The Latest Thing"

TygerTyger: "The Morning Is Quiet"

The Washington Post: "CO_2"

Watcher of the Skies: Poems about Space and Aliens: "Compared to What?"

Contents

The Red Ear Blows Its Nose

The Red Ear Blows Its Nose

My Brain

I'm proud of my brain.
It's bursting with bunches
of concepts and inklings
and notions and hunches,
and lots of big numbers
it expertly crunches,
and facts and opinions
it nibbles and munches . . .
all while my forehead
so thoughtfully scrunches.

Colors

If I could go inside your head
    and use your eyes to see,
I wonder if what you call red
    would look like red to me.

Inside your head, perhaps I'd think
    what looks like red to you
resembles more a shade of pink—
    or purple mixed with blue.

I cannot solve this mystery.
    Are colors just a name?
If I were you, and you were me,
    would we see things the same?

It's All Me

I've sometimes been someone,
sometimes been no one,

the fast-as-they-come one,
the lazy and slow one,

sometimes the chum one,
sometimes the foe one,

the sit-and-be-mum one,
the stand-up-and-crow one,

the hopelessly dumb one,
the cool in-the-know one,

the moping and glum one,
the cheeks-all-aglow one,

the bang-on-a-drum one,
the volume-down-low one,

the merely humdrum one,
the big-fancy-show one,

the I've-no-green-thumb one,
the I-make-things-grow one,

the place-where-I'm-from one,
the place-where-I-go one.

Winning

Though losing
is gruesome
and winning
is winsome
I win some
and lose some
and losing
I wince some

then hold up
my chin some
and thicken
my skin some
and soon
I am winning
and once again
grin some

What's Mine

Things that no one's said before
include, "The red ear blows its nose,"
"I noodled waffles to the door,"
"The slipper broke my shoulder's toes,"

"But what about the squiggly spoon
that ate a penguin's piece of pie
beneath a buttered slice of moon
beyond a sloppy slab of sky?"

Though almost everything's been **said,**
"How sad the pizza's climbed the **peak**
and cheese now tops the oyster bed,"
are words I am the first to speak.

And surely if I say the fox
has cartwheeled through the slide trombone
in search of nylon bowling socks,
these words belong to me alone.

The Horse Who Said Moo

There once was a horse who refused to say *neigh*.
Ask him a question, he'd answer with *moo*.
He didn't give milk, and he loved to eat hay.
But starting when he was a young foal, he knew,

the first time he heard a cow speak to a cow,
that neighing and whinnying just wouldn't do.
"Let dogs say *woof woof* and let cats say *meow*,"
he told himself then, "but this horse will say *moo*."

Did his parents get angry? They sure did, and how!
"*We* both say *neigh*, why can't you say *neigh*, too?
Haven't you noticed that you're not a cow?"
"Of course," he said, not with a *neigh* but a *moo*,

"but mooing alone does not make me a cow.
Watch me! I still love to gallop and trot.
I even enjoy being hitched to a plow!
But do I enjoy saying *neigh*? I do not."

His parents relented. "Fine, then, say *moo*.
Meow if you want to. Oink, roar, or bray.
If it makes you happy, say *cock-a-doodle-doo*.
Just be a proud horse and you need not say *neigh*."

I'm Igserious!

If "ignoble" means "not noble,"
    it seems to me that "ig"
should make *all* words their opposites.
    You're "small"? No, you're igbig!

For "empty," why not say igfull?
    For "dark," why not iglight?
For "ugly," try igbeautiful,
    for "left," why not igright?

I am not "dirty"! I'm igclean!
    "Embarrassed"? No, igproud!
When I am hidden, I'm igseen.
    When quiet, I'm igloud!

Someday when I have igshrunk up
    (make that igshrunk igdown!)
I'll be igpoor and igunknown
    (the thought makes me igfrown).

The world will igignore me then,
    since igno one will dig
the fun I've igdeprived them of
    iglearning them to ig.

The Chorus of Doris

If Morris's chorus is better than Boris's,
Boris's chorus can outsing Dolores's,
Dolores's chorus is better than Horace's,
and Horace's chorus is better than Doris's,
can Doris's chorus be better than Morris's?

The answer, of course, is the chorus of Doris
has got to be worse than the chorus of Morris
because it's no match for the chorus of Horace,
which can't be compared to Dolores's chorus,
which isn't quite up to the chorus of Boris,
which can't sing as well as the chorus of Morris.

But sources assure us that Doris's chorus is
not one to bore us, regardless of Morris's.
Though you would enjoy a performance by Horace's,
Morris's, Boris's, even Dolores's,
you'd also endorse a performance by Doris's,
provided, of course, you enjoy hearing choruses.

Supposing You Were Me

You'd use my mouth
to eat and drink.
You'd use my brain
to have a think.

If you caught cold,
you'd blow my nose.
To take your picture,
I would pose.

You'd use my voice
to raise a cheer.
To listen up,
you'd use my ear.

For standing tall,
you'd use my feet.
You'd use my tush
to take a seat.

If I drank water,
you would pee.
(That is, supposing
you were me.)

Compared to What?

A pebble isn't all that big
    compared to stones or boulders,
but it's a mountain to the ant
    who lifts it on his shoulders.

And if you were a molecule,
    an atom or a proton,
a water drop would be a lake
    for you to sail your boat on.

An elephant is huge for sure;
    its trunk would crush your scale.
And yet it doesn't seem that large
    if you're a humpback whale.

I've always claimed the Earth is huge,
    and no one has denied it.
And yet the Sun alone could **hold**
    a million Earths inside it.

Then certainly the *Sun* is huge?
    Well no, wait just a minute!
The star Mu Cephei could contain
    a billion Suns within it!

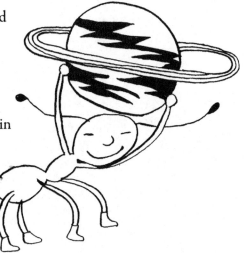

Can we agree Mu Cephei's huge?
    The biggest of Red Giants,
it's dwarfed in size by galaxies!
    Believe me! This is science!

The galaxy that it calls home,
    our own, the Milky Way,
contains a hundred billion stars.
    Mu Cephei's *one*, okay?

And though Mu Cephei dwarfs the Sun,
    is bigger and more shiny,
compare it to the Milky Way
    and you will think it's tiny.

And so it goes. The Milky Way,
    astronomers inform us,
although at first it may appear
    mind-bogglingly enormous,

is hardly bigger than a speck,
    when all is said and done.
Of billions and billions of galaxies,
    the Milky Way's just one.

So when you're asked if something's big,
    say, "I will answer, but . . .
before I do, please tell me this . . .
    Big? Compared to *what*?"

Bang?

When the Big Bang banged
there was nobody near it.
No one existed
so no one could hear it,

and there was no air
to be anywhere found,
nothing to vibrate
or carry the sound.

So how can they say
when the universe sprang
from nothing to something
it made a big bang?

Brain Break

It's quiet now inside my head.
   Not much is brewing there.
My brain is on a break today,
   without a thought or care.

No inklings and no notions
   spin round inside this globe;
silence drapes a quilt of hush
   on each off-duty lobe.

Tomorrow I might call on it
   to think a thought or two,
to solve a riddle, turn a phrase,
   to mutter something true,

to wonder how a bird can fly,
   to ponder till I ache.
Today, though, I won't even try.
   My brain is on a break.

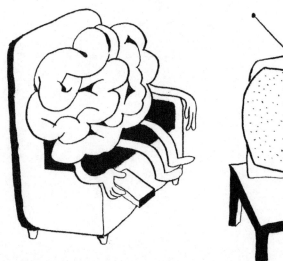

Break In

I had a thought the other day.
But where it came from, I can't say.

Here's the scene: I'm all alone.
The door is locked, I have no phone.

I'm sealed off from the world outside.
You couldn't reach me if you tried.

Then all at once, between my ears,
a sneaky little thought appears!

I'd never had that thought before,
of that I am completely sure,

and so it makes my poor head spin
to wonder how that thought got in.

My Personal Brain

The world that I see
   with my eyes is so dull
compared to the world
   that I see in my skull.
The words that I speak
   with my mouth can't explain
the way that I feel
   in my personal brain.

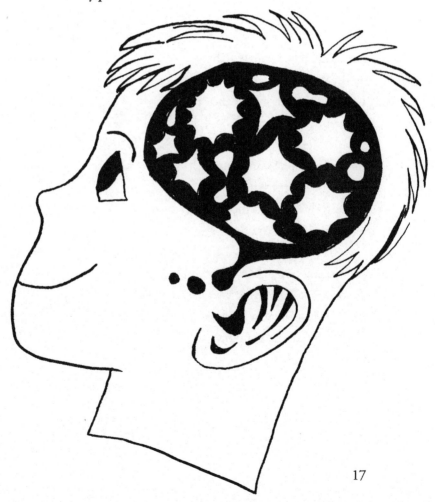

Mistaken Identity

I used to think the moon was just
    the sun when it was tired
and did not have the strength to shine
    but had not yet expired,

and when the sun came back, I thought,
    it was the moon made strong
by sleep and rest to shine again
    in brilliance all day long.

But then, one day, I glanced above.
    The sky was bright and cheery,
and I could see both moon and sun.
    Well, so much for my theory!

I later learned the shining moon
    reflects the shining sun,
and though the sun and moon are two
    the shining is just one,

and so, it seems, what I had thought
    was sort of, kind of, right:
our moon is just the way our sun
    shines down on us at night.

Looking Up

The pictures I imagine there
    would make an artist proud:
castles, whales, and dinosaurs
    and faces in a crowd . . .
but sometimes when I'm looking up
    I find I'm just as wowed
imagining no scene at all
    but seeing only cloud.

Question

When livestock salesmen cannot sleep,
do they lie in bed discounting sheep?

Just Wondering

For there to be a butterfly
must the caterpillar die?
Or does the caterpillar brain
in the butterfly remain?

Not Not Dancing

I will not dance.
　No way, no how!
But wait! I'm on
　my toes right now!
My arms are swinging
　to the beat
which makes me move
　my hips and feet
and twirls me round
　like some mad top,
and though I try
　my best to stop
I do not seem
　to stand a chance.
The music plays.
　I can't *not* dance!

I can't not dance
　although I try.
My knees lift up,
　my elbows fly.
My arms go out,
　my arms go in,
I shake my head,
　I jut my chin,
my shoulders roll,
　my fingers snap,
I slap my thigh,
　my shoes go tap.
I've been bewitched.
　I'm in a trance.
When music plays,
　I can't not dance.

Dopey

I'm just a dopey little poem.
Who thought me up, and why?
I do not have a truth to tell.
I do not have a lie.
I am the wind that bends no tree.
I am the passerby.
I live when I am said out loud,
and when I'm not, I die.

I'm just a mouth with drying lips
that hum a jaunty tune.
The snoring ghost of midnight,
the squinting ghost of noon.
I am the shadow of the clock
beneath a shining moon.
I'm just a dopey little poem.
You found me out too soon.

Instrumental

It's just a piece of polished wood
that holds a bunch of strings.
It has no soul like you and me.
It's from the world of things.
But when an artist picks it up
and touches it just right . . .
that soul I said it didn't have?
On second thought, it might.

Reaching Six

When I was four
I thought that five
was oh so long
to be alive,

but now at six,
I can report
the span of five
is oh so short.

I know the span
of six is long,
yet seven whispers
I am wrong,

and when I'm eight
I guess I'll think
that seven years
are just a blink.

Everything changes.
Nothing sticks.
Today, however,
I'm old at six.

CO$_2$

It may strike you as strange, but it's true:
when you breathe you breathe out CO$_2$,
  and so it may be
   that some plant or some tree
made a leaf from what came out of you.

Breath

I *love* to breathe. I really do.
Not just to stay alive.
I'd keep on breathing even if
I somehow could survive
without a single taste of air.
When all is said and done,
I love the whoosh, I love the feel.
To me it's just plain fun!

Lights Out

I am abed.
The door's ajar.
In dreams ahead
I'll sail afar,

adrift aboard
a ship ashake—
but safe ashore
when I awake.

Worlds

I visit worlds
    when I'm asleep,
worlds I do not
    get to keep—
so rich, so real,
    so true, and yet,
I wash, I dress,
    and I forget.

What I Think

The day is darker than the night.
  The stars don't shine or glimmer.
The Sun is smaller than the Moon . . .
  and colder, too, and dimmer.

The Earth is flat and does not spin.
  Atoms are not small.
Gravity lifts all thing up.
  You cannot bounce a ball.

Birds can't fly. They just pretend.
  Flowers do not grow.
Don't believe the myth of wind.
  There's no such thing as snow.

There's no such thing as rain that falls.
  Gorillas are not strong.
It's what I think. It's how I feel.
  Of course, I could be wrong.

Yours Alone

I'm fabulous and wonderful!
    Okay, perhaps I boast.
Be honest, though. In all the world,
    don't you love *you* the most?

Just pause a bit and think it out,
    then tell me it's not true.
You're *dazzled* by the miracle
    that you alone are you!

Your eyes can see! Your ears can hear!
    You have a working brain!
There's so much going on inside
    that no one can explain!

How did you get to be yourself?
    What *are* you? You're so fine!
You think the world is yours alone.
    But I think that it's mine!

Unlucky

I'm an unlucky fella,
　　there is no doubt.
　　　　I bought an umbrella,
　　　　we had a drought.

I bought a hanky,
　　my nose didn't run.
　　　　I bought a burger,
　　　　　then lost my bun.

I bought a spare tire,
　　then got no flat.
　　　　I bought a ball,
　　　　　then broke my bat.

I bought a coffin.
　　It's worth a try.
　　　　With my bad luck,
　　　　I might not die.

Adjustable Nose

A nose that grows when I tell a lie
is something I would gladly try,
provided it would then retract
whenever I spoke only fact.

I could be wrong, but when it's long
my nose would work so **well**
that I would smell a **thousand scents**
a small nose could not **smell,**

but if I told the truth about
the new scents I'd explore,
my nose would shrink **to normal size**
and smell those scents **no more.**

Sky

How high is the sky?
Good question! Yet I
would much rather know
not how high, but how low.
If I stand on a chair
with my hands in the air,
is it sky that I'm in?
Where does it *begin*?

Solar Lunacy

The moon's more useful than the sun,
though sometimes it wanes and sometimes it waxes.
I'd pick the moon if I could pick only one
heavenly body that spins on its axis.

The moon shines when it's dark, and so
it's useful in helping us find our way.
The sun provides its warmth and glow
when we don't need it much: by day.

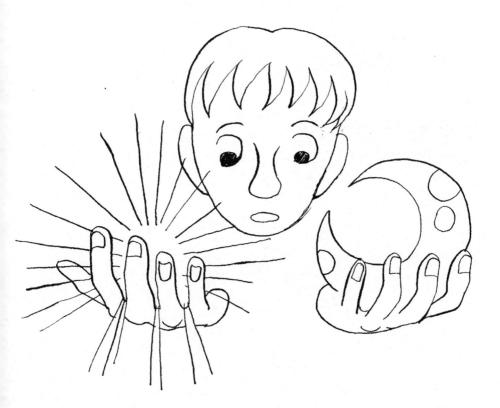

Nosy Advice

No matter that your nose may sport
a patch of pimples or a wart,
no matter if it's long or short,
if you would sniffle, sneeze, or snort,
a nose of any kind or sort
deserves your full, complete support.

And so I say to everyone,
from astronaut to poet:
Hold your nose in high esteem,
and don't be slow to show it.
You only get one nose in life,
so make sure you don't blow it.

My Nose

Whoever thought up where to put
    the pieces of my face
must have loved my nose because
    it holds a central place.

My ears are way off to the sides,
    my mouth down by my chin,
my eyes are to the left and right
    (they twinkle when I grin),

and yet my nose, I'm proud to say,
    is like a meeting place
for up and down, for left and right,
    and unifies my face.

It may be small. It may be little.
    Agreed, it's not that large.
But there it sniffs, smack in the middle,
    as if it were in charge.

Fabulous Five

Let's hear it for the ear!
Its every word is sound.
To know what's coming, **always keep**
your ear against the grou**nd.**

Let's honk it for the nose!
It sniffs at common scents.
It learns before the eye w**hen skunks**
have slipped inside the fence.

Let's twist it for the tongue!
It wags with such good ta**ste.**
Tongues are quick to lick **the bowl**
so nothing goes to waste.

Let's focus on the eye!
The eye is out of sight.
But only when its lid is cl**osed**
or on the darkest night.

Let's feel it for the skin!
It has the common touch.
Without it you would no**t enjoy**
mom's kisses half as much.

Let's celebrate all five!
Ears eyes nose tongue an**d skin!**
If not for them how could we hope
to know the world we're in?

Mouth Mouthing Off

I am the mansion
of your tongue,
the castle where
your songs get sung.

Use me for speaking
and chattering, but . . .
remember that sometimes
I serve you best shut.

My Champion Bee

My bee's in the biz
   of buzzing and is
      the world's greatest wiz
         at creating a buzz.
            She's the best that there was
               and the best that there is.

She zags and she zigs,
   she zips and she zooms
      on flowers and twigs
         full of zinnia blooms.
            No one asks, *Is she*
               sufficiently busy?

My bee's in a tizzy.
   She's making me dizzy.
      Her thorax is fuzzy.
         I love her because she
            hums without singing
               and doesn't like stinging.

Her business is buzzin'.
   She sucks from a dozen
      flowers her cousin
         the fly never was in.
            The blooms that she's chosen
               to stick her bee-nose in

are those pollen grows in
and sweet nectar flows in.
She hovers there, frozen,
as if she were posin'
but she's only sipping
to fuel still more zipping

and zagging and zooming
after resuming
her dance through the blooming
blossoms perfuming
throughout honey season
the garden my bee's in.

To Be an Ant

I'd like to be a little ant
who scurries on the ground
and always seems in such a rush
to get where he is bound.

There'd be a crumb upon my back
that fell from some kid's plate,
and though it's just a speck to him
it's twenty times my weight.

I'd bear the heavy load with ease,
I'd march along with pep,
and all I'd ask of you is *Please!*
I beg you! Watch your step!

Army Ants

How can there be army ants?
They're simply too minute.
Though ants can march, I'm pretty sure
they cannot wear a boot.
They cannot stand up on two legs
 and solemnly salute.
And I have never seen a gun
so small an ant could shoot.

Skin Deep

My zebra often whines and gripes
how bored she is with having stripes.
She says she's jealous of the leopard
whose fur with dots and spots is peppered.

My leopard's jealous in reverse:
he thinks that dots and spots are worse,
and gladly he would trade them in
to wear the stripes of zebra skin.

I tell my zebra having fur
with stripes looks marvelous on her.
I tell my leopard he should not
deny the beauty of the dot.

And in the end, they both agree.
At least, they say, they're not like me,
without a pattern or design.
How rude they are, these pets of mine!

Bird Talk

The eagle said,
"Wake up and fly!
Be bold and give
your wings a try!"
The penguin answered
with a sigh,
"I never cared
that much for sky.
Sure, it's pretty,
vast and blue,
but on the ground
it's pretty too.
I thank you for
your point of view,
but I'll do me
and you do you."

Jokes Talk Back

1. *The Chicken*
Human beings must be mad!
They must be bored and lonely.
There's so much to discuss and yet
they seem to want to only

chat about the street I crossed
and wonder what possessed me.
I guess it's better that they talk
about me than digest me.

2. *The Fireman*
I'm sick of people asking me
about my red suspenders.
For me the question tops the list
of conversation enders.

But if you want to guarantee
a conversation stopped,
just say I stuck my feet in flames
to see my corns get popped.

3. *The Elephant*

Can you tell time? Then tell me this:
What time is it when I
stretch out to lounge upon a fence
and gaze up at the sky?

You think it's time to fix the fence?
No, my friend, you're wrong.
I gave up peanuts, lost a ton.
Besides, the fence is strong.

It can be any time at all.
There's no way you can tell.
I love to watch the sky by day
but midnight works as well.

Take It or Leave It

They say that it may rain today
    but the sky looks clear right now.
Should I leave my new umbrella home
    or bring it anyhow?

I'd hate to lug the thing all day
    if there's no rain at all,
but what if I leave my umbrella home
    and rain begins to fall?

What if I'm standing in the street
    and sneezing, sopping wet,
saying, "Why did I leave my umbrella home?"
    I'd feel like a fool, and yet

what if it doesn't rain? I wish
    I knew a way to tell.
I think I'll leave my umbrella home . . .
    and I'll stay home as well.

Just a Thought

I never thought that I would think
the thoughts I think I might have thought.
I think the thoughts I think, but think
they're not the thoughts I think I ought.

We Come in Peace

Dear Earthlings,

By now you've seen our spaceships
as they hover in your sky.
We've traveled far to get here,
and I guess you wonder why.

We come in peace to meet you,
here on Earth, away from home.
Our reasons will be clear enough
once you have read this poem.

On Mars we speak a language
that's like English, but reversed,
so *black* is *white* on Mars
and *good* is *bad*
and *last* is *first*,

and when we say
we're sitting down
it means *we're standing up,*
and when we say *the dog is old*
it means *he's just a pup.*

Delicious means *it tastes like dirt.*
I'm thrilled means *I am bored.*
Up means *down*
and *heal* means *hurt*
and *hated* means *adored.*

And when we say *we've gone berserk*
it means *we're calm and staid.*
So when I said we come in peace
it meant

WE WILL INVADE!

The Latest Thing

I have invented the thingamajig.
It looks like a whatchamacallit.
Can you imagine a gizmo this big
that folds up and fits in your wallet?

With buttons and switches controlled by your thumbs,
with gears and a long metal arm,
it does what it does as it quietly hums
or it squeals like a burglar alarm.

The world's never known a contraption like this,
the finest that there ever was!
People will love it! I'm sure it can't miss!
Too bad I don't know what it does.

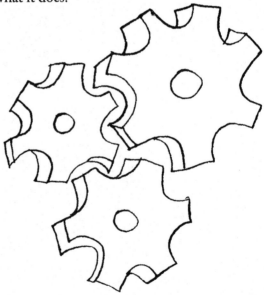

This Poem Is New

This poem is new. I made it up.
    Before I sat and wrote it,
you could not read this poem at all,
    recite its lines or quote it.

It did not rhyme, it had no words,
    you could not sing or hum it.
If there's a Mountain of What's Not,
    this poem was at the summit,

the King of What Had Never Been,
    to Not Yet There, a hero,
the empty space you find within
    the circle of a zero.

But now this poem exists for sure,
    so please feel free to read it!
It's on the Mountain of What Is
    in case you ever need it.

And someday when this poem is old,
    remember that this doesn't
mean there wasn't once a time
    when it most surely wasn't.

Unplanned Poem

I started writing. Had no plan,
  with nothing much to say.
What mattered was that I began.
  This poem was underway.

I kept on writing, bit by bit,
  and paid no mind to whether
there was any sense to it.
  I threw these words together,

and suddenly, out of the blue,
  though I don't understand it,
this poem has found its way to you . . .
  exactly as I planned it.

Beyond Compare

A circle colored in with chalk,
a football someone kicked too high,
a night-light making dim from dark,
a peephole cut out from the sky,
an eye without the middle part,
a head without a bit of hair,
a canvas waiting to be art,
a sun, except without the glare.

A clock without the moving hands,
a coin without the royal face,
a wheel that's given up its spins,
a doily cut from cotton lace.

I try my best to liken it
to something else. A loose balloon?
But no. It's nothing but itself.
The dizzy, lovely, perfect Moon.

The Moon Fell Down

The moon fell down.
It landed in the street in front of my house.
It was much smaller than anyone had expected,
though nonetheless beautiful
with its thousands of craters
and creamy color of burnished marble.

It was slightly taller than a tree
and wide enough to block traffic in both directions.
We gathered around it and wondered whom to call.
The mayor? An astronomer?
Is there a person in charge of the tides?
My mother told me not to get too close.
I believe I saw Neil Armstrong's footprints
along with leftover pieces of the lunar module,
which looked as tiny as a toy.

And later that night, when my mother wasn't looking,
I went out front and touched the moon.
My mother saw the dust on my fingers when I returned
and knew I had disobeyed.

She told the moon, "You'll have to go home now."
The moon then rose back into the sky
where it remains to this day.

Moon Mint

If the moon were a mint, I would open up wide,
cramming the whole candy moon mint inside

and swallowing every last moon rock and crater.
I wonder, though, what I would make of it later?

I guess I'd be sad when I looked up at night
and noticed no moon shining down with its light,

but still I'd console myself greatly by thinking:
the moon may be gone but my breath isn't stinking.

Boredom Break

I'm very, very bored.
I'm sitting in a chair.
I'm bored out of my gourd.
And I don't really care.
I spent all day in school
so now I can afford
ten minutes by myself,
magnificently bored.

Oh look, I have two thumbs.
I'll twiddle them, I guess.
And then I'll scratch my nose.
I'm bored, but I confess
it's what I want to be.
Not always, but for now.
I'm very, very bored,
but loving it somehow.

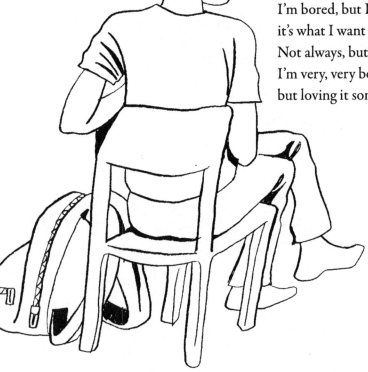

Popcorn Dream

Last night I had the strangest dream!
While boating on a lake,
I felt the ship begin to crunch,
the deck begin to shake!

The water that I sailed upon
had disappeared somehow,
and in its place, to my surprise,
as I looked past the bow,

the lake was filled with yellow puffs
on which my ship was borne!
I scarcely could believe my eyes!
Who popped this magic corn?

I thought of just one thing to do.
"Abandon ship!" I cried.
And as I headed overboard,
my mouth was open wide.

Not a Children's Poem

This poem is not a children's poem.
   It's grown-ups who should read it.
It offers tons of great advice,
   but kids don't really need it.

Don't dump your garbage in the sea.
   Do not pollute the air!
Be sure the water that we drink
   is clean and always there.

Fomenting war is bad. Make peace!
   Don't let the world get blown up.
You know this. You don't need this poem.
   Unless you are a grown-up.

The Thing about Chickens

When chickens squawking in the coop
squat down on their chicken legs
they're sometimes making chicken poop
and sometimes making chicken eggs.

If you are smart you'll make darn sure
you know which one your chicken's makin',
since eggs will please you rather more
than poop with orange juice and bacon.

Why Can't an Elephant?

A bird purred
though it wasn't allowed.
Then a cat said **oink**
and a dog me**owed**.
A bat said neigh
and a tiger chirped.
But my favorite **part**?
A bumblebee **burped**!

A bumblebee **burped**
as a spider snored
and a pig went **tweet**
and a turtle roared,
and a camel brayed
to a sparrow's **croak**,
as I mooed and **laughed**
at a goat's bad **joke**.

I'm just being **silly**.
I'm guessing **you know**.
None of this **happened**.
It's not how **things go**.
We can't change **our sounds**.
Our voices are **stuck**.
Don't expect **hoots**
when you speak **with a duck**.

But why shouldn't tadpoles
bellow or bark?
Why shouldn't frogs
make a gobbly remark?
Who made the rules up?
Who wrote the law?
Why can't an elephant
quack or hee-haw?

What Am I?

I'm what's left inside the box
  when everything is gone.
I'm what you are wearing when
  you have no clothing on.

I'm what you remember
  when you can't recall a thing.
I'm what's left of winter
  when the calendar says spring.

I am that which you love more
  than that which you love most.
I'm what haunts the haunted house
  abandoned by its ghost.

I am what you find between
  two surfaces that touch.
I'm what's less than anything.
  I've never been too much.

May I Go to the Circus?

When I was only five years old,
   my mom and dad were cruel.
They taught me words they knew were wrong,
   then sent me off to school.

One day in class I raised my hand.
   The teacher called on me.
"May I go to the circus now?"
   I meant I had to pee,

but mom and dad had made me think
   a circus was a toilet.
The teacher said, "I'm teaching now,
   you wise guy! Please don't spoil it!"

I clutched myself and said, "But please!
   I really have to go!"
The teacher pointed to the door
   and said, "Enjoy the show!"

The Just-Because Hug

Bears will hug you 'cause they're mean,
    so watch out for their claws!
But I don't hug you 'cause I'm nice.
    I hug you just because.

There is no rule that says I must.
    There are no "hugging laws,"
no hidden motives to discuss.
    I hug you just because.

I do not hug you to reward
    your virtues or your flaws.
Can you guess the reason why
    I hug you? Just because.

When life's too busy, rushing by,
    sometimes I like to pause
and wrap my arms around you. Why?
    I hug you just because.

Just because I have two arms.
    Be glad it's not two paws!
Just because it feels so good,
    I hug you. Just because.

Obviously

For Lincoln

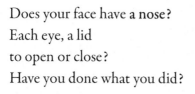

Does corn have a cob?
Do birds have a beak?
Do doors have a knob?
Mountains, a peak?

Does your face have a nose?
Each eye, a lid
to open or close?
Have you done what you did?

Does your school have a teacher?
The sun ever set?
Is a lion a creature?
Is water wet?

Are clouds ever white?
The sky ever blue?
Do owls love the night?
Does your daddy love you?

Alphabet Takes

1.
Can you recite the alphabet
    the way the selfish do?
Shout out loud the letter I
    but barely whisper U.

2.
The alphabet begins with A,
    and that seems right to me,
but when it comes to how it ends,
    I always ask, Y Z?

3.
The letter V stood by the door
    and paused to let me through.
I said, "But I must follow H.
    You're V. So after U."

4.
My mother says the alphabet
   real fast through S so she
has time enough to pause a bit
   and pour herself some T.

5.
When I was taught the alphabet,
   back when I was young,
I worried when I got to B
   that maybe I'd be stung.

6.
A sailor says the alphabet,
   unlike you and me,
a bit afraid that he might get
   forever lost at C.

Reading between the Letters

The alphabet says HI
between the G and J,
but never says GOODBYE.
I guess it plans to stay.

Just ask it, "Will you go?"
Then skip ahead and see.
The alphabet says NO
between the M and P.

ELEMENO

When oh when oh
I was young
and L-M-N-O-
P was sung

there's something that I
did not then know:
there is no letter
elemeno!

Dancing

The music enters through my ears
   and runs down to my feet.
All at once it lifts my heels
   and makes them tap the beat,
then journeys upward past my knees
   where gracefully it grips
the muscles that I use to make
   a swivel in my hips,

and now there is no doubt at all:
   I'm in a dancing spell.
You only have to look at me,
   the way I move, to tell:
I'm swaying back and forth, I twirl,
   I shimmy, bob my head.
The music came in through my ears,
   but look where it has led!

Moon Cheese

Of *course* the moon is made of cheese,
   but can you tell me this?
Is it made of Chèvre, Cheddar, Brie,
   or maybe Swiss?

I really need to know right now,
   since if it's made of Chèvre,
my favorite cheese, I'm taking off
   and living there forever.

I'll pack a million crackers
   and I'll bring a tiny knife
to smear the cheese across each one
   and live a happy life.

But if it's made of Cheddar, Brie,
   or Swiss, I will not go!
If there's no Chèvre on the moon,
   I'm staying here below.

Under the Rainbow

Under the rainbow,
on top of the ground,
that's where the puddles
we splash in are found,

that's where the petals
are sparkling with drops,
after the downpour
and thundering stops.

Way up above now
the sun's broken through,
brilliant as always,
the sky again blue.

Don't you just love it?
The cloudburst, and then
sunshine and rainbows,
the world new again?

They Say

They say the morning's broken,
  but it looks fine to me.
There's not a crack in all the sky,
  no damage I can see.
The world appears as good as new,
  the sun shines just as strong.
The grass awakes to morning dew,
  the birds resume their song.
They say the morning's broken.
  But I say they are wrong.

They say the night has fallen.
  Will someone tell me why?
The stars are where they were before.
  The moon is just as high.
There are no pieces on the ground
  of what was once the night.
And if it fell, it made no sound
  when crashing from its height.
They say the night has fallen,
  but how can that be right?

Thank You, Nose

It rumbles loudly when I doze.
It sometimes strikes a snooty pose.
And when I catch a cold, it flows.
Yet when I stop to smell a rose,
life's frantic hustle-bustle slows
and such a joy inside me grows
that from my head down to my toes
my favorite thing on earth's my nose.

The Thing about Breezes

On a hot summer day
when you feel a breeze blow,
is it saying goodbye,
or saying hello?

Is it saying "I'm here"
or saying "I'm gone"?
Does it mean "I've arrived"
or "I have moved on"?

You can't pin it down.
A breeze will not say.
A breeze can't arrive
without racing away.

The Breeze

The sail was tall above our heads.
    It billowed in the breeze.
It launched us out beyond the pier
    to sail the seven seas.

The breeze itself could not be seen,
    a phantom made of air.
And yet it moved our boat so fast
    we knew that it was there.

It ferried us to distant worlds
    beyond the ocean's foam,
And then, when it was time to rest,
    it took us safely home.

Autumn Leaves

They fall from the trees
but a wind happens by
so they do not head downward
but rise to the sky

where they dance in the sun
in a dizzying show
of color and light
as we watch **from below**

Listen, I'm **hearing**
a fluttering **sound**
as leaves born **on treetops**
make peace **with the ground**

Summer Sorcerer

I'm something of a sorcerer.
  Last fall I cast this spell:
"May every leaf upon that tree
  fall down!" And down they fell!

When winter came, I then proclaimed,
  "Warm weather, time to go!"
And suddenly, the air grew chill.
  My yard filled up with snow.

When spring arrived, I thought it time
  to test my magic powers:
"Snow, be gone! Warmth, return!"
  My garden filled with flowers.

And now that summer's here at last,
  my favorite spell of all:
I've made new leaves for when I cast
  my spell to make them fall.

Spring in My Step

They say there's a "spring in my step,"
　　but I've always wondered how come a
spring in one's step is so common,
　　but never a winter or summer?

And why is there never an autumn?
　　It seems like a curious thing.
No matter the season we're having,
　　my steps always think it is spring.

The Morning Is Quiet

The morning is quiet.
There's nothing I hear.
I think there's a riot
of hush in my ear,

a growl that is purring,
a sleep without snoring,
a monster not stirring,
a lion not roaring,

a shaking that's steady,
a wave that's not breaking.
I'm rested and ready.
It's time to be waking.

My First Snow

Before it snows the world is gray,
   the leaves are off the trees;
the sun won't drive the cold away
   or warm the wintry breeze;

and all the world seems pale and flat,
   a stage without a show;
a gloomy, drab unwelcome mat.
    But wait! What's that? It's snow!

The snowflakes fill the frosty air
   and sparkle as they're swirled,
and soon the world's not dark or bare.
   It's like a whole new world,

a world that's neither old nor gray
   but lively, bright, and new.
They *told* me snow was beautiful.
   And now I know it's true.

Better Late than Never

Last year the spring came early. My snowman faced his doom.
The birds were still in Florida as trees began to bloom

and warmth returned to push aside the winter in its prime.
Last year the spring came early. It's coming late this time.

The birds who are returning find their nesting branches bare,
and some have never glimpsed before a snowman's coal-eyed stare.

My snowman gives the birds a wink, then melts away at last.
The nascent blossoms burst their buds. And winter's finally past.

The Cold Poem

This poem regrets it did not put
a thicker sweater on.
It dreamed of spring and quite forgot
that winter's not yet gone.

It dreamed of April's gentle sprouts
and left without a coat.
How could it have forgotten spring
remains as yet remote?

It dreamed of frost becoming dew,
of birds returning home,
but it forgot that dreams of spring
can't melt a frozen poem.

Fall and Winter

Day by day
the daylight shrinks,
but then just when
the whole world thinks

the daylight's bound
to disappear,
help arrives.
Winter's here.

Unlikely hero,
how it snows!
But day by day
the daylight grows.

Rondel

Translated from the French of Charles, duc d'Orléans (1394–1465)

The earth has shed its overcoat
of freezing rain and drifting snow
and changed into the lighter clothes
the sun at last returned to sew.

The beasts and birds are thrilled to trill
the song of sunlight's welcome glow:
The earth has shed its overcoat
of freezing rain and drifting snow.

On streams and rivers you may note
the silver fabric of the season.
People sing, and here's the reason
sunken spirits rise and float:
The earth has shed its overcoat.

Dog in Winter

To be a dog in winter means
to bark up trees that have no leaves,
to scratch behind the ears of dawn
while doing tricks no cat conceives,

to walk in circles every time
you're fixing to lie down in snow,
to listen as the half-moon howls
to feel the earth eclipse its glow,

and yet, as it befits your breed,
you face the ice that winter sends
at ease within the leash of need
that binds you to your snowman friends.

Winter's Tale

Because it was winter, the snowflakes were glad.
With six legs apiece, they all danced.
They sparkled and swirled and cavorted like mad
as the murderous springtime advanced,

and glaciers were melting, but healed when they froze,
and branches were dreaming of blooming,
and bears were enjoying a wintertime doze,
and plants were for now unassuming,

when out of the dark, as the sun spewed its glare,
there were songs that nobody had written,
and somebody heard a young mother declare
that her daughter had lost her left mitten.

Riddle

Up in the sky
you've always found me.
The world itself
revolves around me.

I give my light
and you absorb it
every moment
of your orbit.

Be glad I do not
disappear.
There'd be no way
to mark the year.

And earth, unanchored,
would be hurled
through cold, dark space.
You're welcome, world.

Summer Breeze

This poem has nothing much to say.
    I'd like to make that clear.
If information's what you seek,
    you will not find it here.

If you are searching for a poem
    to stimulate your mind,
I might as well be frank with you:
    this poem is not that kind.

You're reading now a piece of fluff,
    a brazen waste of time
consisting of some random words
    and packaged as a rhyme.

It's like a little breeze that blows
    and rustles through your hair.
It's likely that you'll soon forget
    this poem was ever there.

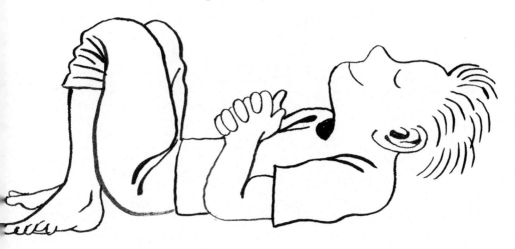

To and Fro

A wind that's blowing
to and fro
is to-and-fro-ing,
as you know,

but did you know
what else it's doing?
The wind is also
fro-and-to-ing.

Fro-and-to-ing,
to-and-fro-ing,
winds are coming,
winds are going.

Which is which?
There is no knowing.
Let's just say
the wind is blowing.

Breezy Does It

The breeze is a creature
that loves loop-de-loops,
soaring and gliding
in daredevil swoops,

elegant cartwheels
through nimbus-y heights,
now-and-then friendships
with eagles or kites,

but me? I'm a creature
with feet on the ground,
happy to be here
all safe and all sound,

and though I might envy
its antics of air,
I love the breeze best
when it rustles my hair.

Reflection

I wonder why the sky is gray,
the grass no longer green,
and why the crystal lake takes on
a trembling silver sheen

in which the trees along the shore
in yellow, gold, maroon,
leave sketches of their leaves beside
the rippling autumn moon?

Dawn

Night sent darkness,
but look what the day sent:
first thing this morning,
a pink glow of nascent

effulgence adorning
the waking horizon
to give us fair warning
the sun would be rising.

Talking to the Wall

I'm talking to the autumn leaves.
   I beg them not to fall.
And yet I know I might as well
   be talking to the wall

because in wondrous waves of red
   and purple, gold, and brown,
the autumn leaves depart the trees
   and flutter gently down.

I'm talking to the winter snow.
   I beg it not to fall.
And yet I know I might as well
   be talking to the wall

because in sheets of silver mist
   the snowflakes fill the air.
Did they not hear a word I said?
   Or did they just not care?

I tell the earth to take a breath.
   Why rush? Why spin at all?
And yet I know I might as well
   be talking to the wall.

Inside

The sun may shine,
the breeze may blow,
the birds may sing,
the trees may grow,
the sky is blue
for all I know.
Who cares? I stay inside.

I have my toys,
I have my phone,
I'm here within
my bedroom zone.
Though others hate
to be alone,
who cares? I stay inside.

Outside the door
my puppy calls:
*Why waste the day
inside of walls?*
He wants to play
with sticks and balls.
Who cares? I stay inside.

But then I get
a text from you!
*I'm in the park!
Can you come, too?*
I'd planned to stay
inside, it's true.
Who cares? I race outside.

Off to Nowhere

I'm off to nowhere,
skipping along,
down by the lakeside,
singing a song,

hearing the wind blow,
tossing a stone,
watching the ripples,
all on my own,

thinking of nothing
except what I see,
except what I'm feeling,
except being me,

down by the lakeside,
skipping along,
heading for nowhere,
singing this song.

The Last Poem in the Book

Eventually each book of poems
    must reach the final stage
when there's just one more poem to read
    upon one final page,

and this book is like all the rest,
    and here's the proof you need.
You'll notice once you've read this poem
    there are none left to read.

S. Federico draws, writes, and lives in New York City with his cat.

Robert Schechter's award-winning poetry for children has appeared in *Highlights for Children, Cricket, Spider, Ladybug,* the *Caterpillar, Blast Off, Countdown, Orbit,* and more than a dozen anthologies published by Bloomsbury, National Geographic, Macmillan, Houghton Mifflin Harcourt, the  Emma Press, and Little, Brown Books for Young Readers. His poems for adults have won both the Willis Barnstone Translation Prize and the X. J. Kennedy Parody Award, and his verse often appears in the Washington Post Style Invitational (where he is a former Rookie and Loser of the Year) and in the *Spectator* magazine's weekly humor competition. Robert is the editor of the children's poetry section of *Better Than Starbucks*. This is his first collection.

Also from Word Galaxy Press

David Alpaugh, *Spooky Action at a Distance – Poems*;
Seeing the There There – Poems

Barbara Lydecker Crane, *You Will Remember Me – Poems*

Daniel Galef, *Imaginary Sonnets – Poems*

Margaret Rockwell Finch, *Crone's Wines – Late Poems*

Emily Grosholz, *The Stars of Earth – New and Selected Poems*;
Traveling, Light and Dark, Discovery and Translation – Essays

A. G. Harmon, *Some Bore Gifts – Stories*

Elizabyth A. Hiscox, *Reassurance in Negative Space – Poems*

Sydney Lea and James Kochalka,
The Exquisite Triumph of Wormboy – Poems and Illustrations

Chukwuma Ndulue, *Holding Rain – Poems*

www.wordgalaxy.com

Printed in Great Britain
by Amazon

21955608R00066